C000175726

1977

Island Music Limited

PLEASE DO NOT
REARRANGE
FURNITURE

OMINATION
TEENAGE
BI-SEXUEL

Exclusive Distributors:
Music Sales Limited
8/9 Frith Street, London W1V 5TZ, England.
Music Sales Pty Limited
120 Rothschild Avenue, Rosebery, NSW 2018, Australia.

Order No.AM939345
ISBN 0-7119-6005-4
This book © Copyright 1996 by
Island Music Limited

Visit the Internet Music Shop at
http://www.musicsales.co.uk

Unauthorised reproduction of
any part of this publication by any
means including photocopying is an
infringement of copyright.

Music arranged by Roger Day.
Music processed by Paul Ewers Music Design.
Book design by Michael Bell Design.

Printed in the United Kingdom by
Halstan & Co. Ltd., Amersham, Bucks.

Your Guarantee of Quality:
As publishers, we strive to produce every book to the
highest commercial standards. The music has been freshly
engraved and, whilst endeavouring to retain the original
running order of the recorded album, the book has been
carefully designed to minimise awkward page turns and to
make playing from it a real pleasure. Particular care has been
given to specifying acid-free, neutral-sized paper made from
pulps which have not been elemental chlorine bleached.
This pulp is from farmed sustainable forests and was
produced with special regard for the environment.
Throughout, the printing and binding have been planned to
ensure a sturdy, attractive publication which should give years
of enjoyment. If your copy fails to meet our high standards,
please inform us and we will gladly replace it.

Music Sales' complete catalogue describes
thousands of titles and is available in full colour
sections by subject, direct from Music Sales Limited.
Please state your areas of interest and send
a cheque/postal order for £1.50 for postage to:
Music Sales Limited, Newmarket Road, Bury St. Edmunds,
Suffolk IP33 3YB.

Lose Control

Words & Music by Mark Hamilton & Tim Wheeler

© Copyright 1996 Island Music Limited, 47 British Grove, London W4.
All Rights Reserved. International Copyright Secured.

Verse 2:
You arrive with cool in your eyes
And explain to me how he makes you feel inside,
So safe, secure.
Later on as night is falling,
You bring me on with violent words,
Desire and being young.

Goldfinger

Words & Music by Tim Wheeler

© Copyright 1996 Island Music Limited, 47 British Grove, London W4.
All Rights Reserved. International Copyright Secured.

to oc - cu - py my mind,— while I'm wait - ing for her.—

To Coda ✛ |1.

molto rall.

|2.

D.%. al Coda

Verse 2:
Down in the basement
Listening to the rain.
Thinking things over,
I think it over again, oh,
Think it over again.

Verse 3:
I'm riding it down,
Listening to the rain.
She'll be here soon
I lie back and drift away, oh,
I lie back and drift away.

Gone The Dream

Words & Music by Tim Wheeler

© Copyright 1996 Island Music Limited, 47 British Grove, London W4.
All Rights Reserved. International Copyright Secured.

fore I went to bed.___ My face in the light,___ il-
lu - mi - na - ted, un - trou - bled___ and safe,___
as your face___ is shin - ing up - on___ me, a love that would nev - er cease.___
___ And out where the cold wind blows,___ it

cold wind blow - ing.

Verse 2:
Hours pass, ticking slowly,
Lying wide awake.
All across the land the lights are out,
Under an open sky.
I feel for you and everybody
Dreaming in your beds.
I'm feeling lost, there is nothing,
Nothing more than this.

Going out where the cold wind blows,
It rocks my childhood sleep.
And up in the starry skies
And further out to sea,
Late in time when it will come,
I see in my dreams.
At night with the cold wind blowing,
At night with the cold wind blowing.

Girl From Mars

Words & Music by Tim Wheeler

© Copyright 1995 Island Music Limited, 47 British Grove, London W4.
All Rights Reserved. International Copyright Secured.

To - day a - sleep in the chair by the win - dow, it felt as if you'd re - turned. I thought that you were stand - ing ov - er me, when I woke there was no one there, I still love you, girl from

28

Mars. D'you re-mem-ber the time— I knew a girl from Mars,— I don't know—

— if you knew— that. Oh, we'd stay up late play-ing cards,— Hen-ry Win-ter-man ci-

D.%. al Coda ⊕ Coda

- gars, though she nev-er— told— me her name.—

Verse 2:
Surging through the darkness and over the moonlit strand,
Electricity in the air.
Twisting all through the night on the terrace,
Now that summer is here.
I know that you are almost in love with me,
I can see it in your eyes.
Strange lights shimmering over the sea tonight.
And it almost blows my mind,
As I look to the stars.

I'd Give You Anything

Words & Music by Tim Wheeler

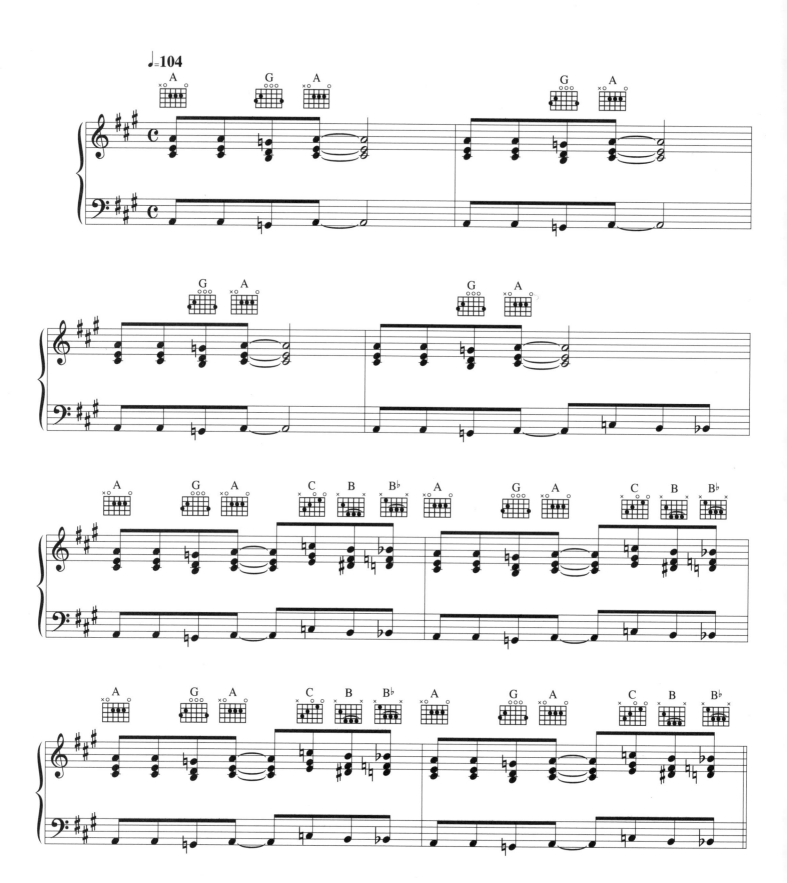

© Copyright 1996 Island Music Limited, 47 British Grove, London W4.
All Rights Reserved. International Copyright Secured.

days seem the same___ and you feel like you're los - ing your mind.___

(1, 2.) The

I

Kung Fu

Words & Music by Tim Wheeler

1. Kung Fu, do___ what you do to me, I have-n't been the same since my teen-age lo-bo-to-my.
(Verses 2 & 3 see block lyric)

Full on, I moved to Hong Kong___ with Bruce Lee's bro-ther and___

© Copyright 1995 Island Music Limited, 47 British Grove, London W4.
All Rights Reserved. International Copyright Secured.

⊕ *Coda*

Verse 2:
Last night Jackie Chan came round,
I played pool with him and we hung out.
Mister Miagi and the X-Men
Called in for a while as well.

Verse 3:
Kung fu, do what you do to me,
I can't live without my Kung Fu movies.
"Shanghai Killers" and "Deadly Road",
My life was ruined when the Green Dragon closed.

Oh Yeah

Words & Music by Tim Wheeler

Oh yeah,— she was tak-ing me ov- er, and oh——— yeah,— it was the

start of the sum - mer.

Ooh ah, ooh ah. 1. On

© Copyright 1996 Island Music Limited, 47 British Grove, London W4.
All Rights Reserved. International Copyright Secured.

42

Verse 2:
Driving her home after midnight
I felt so good, everything was alright,
Her thoughts seemed lost in the night sky,
I remember everything.
I don't know why these things ever end,
I sometimes wish it was that summer again,
I still see her in my sleep,
And hear the sighing of the summer wind.
Still I don't regret one thing.

43

Let It Flow

Words & Music by Tim Wheeler

© Copyright 1996 Island Music Limited, 47 British Grove, London W4.
All Rights Reserved. International Copyright Secured.

(1, 3.) Here she comes walk-ing 'cross the sand, she'll nev-er know how she
(Verse 2 see block lyric)

blows my mind. She's there with the che - mi - cals

in my brain, spin-ning soft-ly round my head. I'm

gon - na give in, I'll nev - er change my mind, I

45

she is al-ways blow-ing my mind.

She's blow-ing my mind,
Look in my eyes,

she is al - ways blow-ing my mind.
she is al - ways blow-ing my mind.

47

I've ev - er known.

Coda

Repeat ad lib.

Verse 2:
The autumn and the winter have been and gone,
Half the time I never knew what was wrong.
I never noticed I was feeling down,
It just went day by day.
She'll never know how she turned it round,
She'll never know how she blows my mind.
It was a long time coming to me,
I'm gonna outshine every star.
She's gonna bring me through.
She's blowing my mind,
She's always blowing my mind.

Innocent Smile

Words & Music by Mark Hamilton

1. Trip-ping round the town as the sun comes down,— flyin' with your friends with the
(Verse 2 see block lyric)

stars a-live.— Trip-pin' round the town as the sun comes down,—

fly-in' with your friends with the stars a-live.— Run-nin' on a high from the

© Copyright 1996 Island Music Limited, 47 British Grove, London W4.
All Rights Reserved. International Copyright Secured.

You turned it all___ a - round,___ it on - ly took your smile,___

swing - ing from a chan - de - lier,___

hang - ing from the sky.___

Verse 2:
Vandalism's fun when there's nothing to do,
Break a few things say it wasn't you.
Vandalism's fun when there's nothing to do,
Break a few things say it wasn't you.
Let it all kick in, take you for a ride,
Strapped to a rocket heading for the sky.
Let it all kick in, take you for a ride,
Strapped to a rocket heading for the sky.

Angel Interceptor

Words & Music by Tim Wheeler & Rick McMurray

© Copyright 1995 Island Music Limited, 47 British Grove, London W4.
All Rights Reserved. International Copyright Secured.

oh to - mor - - - - row you're com - - ing

(home.)

I feel

1, 2, 3.   **4.**   *D.%. al Coda*   ⊕ *Coda*

hea - ven in you,

Verse 2:
Sitting alone
With the TV on.
I fell asleep,
I was hoping you'd call.
And I dreamed
We were dancing in the dark
Really slow.

Lost In You

Words & Music by Tim Wheeler

1. Ly - ing wide a - wake
(Verse 2 see block lyric)

un - der strange skies, want - ing to call you but it is late at night.

© Copyright 1996 Island Music Limited, 47 British Grove, London W4.
All Rights Reserved. International Copyright Secured.

Coda

Verse 2:

Staring at the wall, I sink inside,
I think about it all, I get caught up in my life.
I can't think straight because it's tearing up my mind.
I feel like I'm on fire, nothing I can do,
I'm troubled with doubt, though I know it is not true.
And it's times like these when I am
Dying to speak to you, dying to get through,
Dying to get through.

Darkside Lightside

Words & Music by Tim Wheeler

© Copyright 1996 Island Music Limited, 47 British Grove, London W4.
All Rights Reserved. International Copyright Secured.

when ev - 'ry - thing___ is gon - na turn out right.___

When all the ans - wers lie be -
Mem - or - ies___ of long

hind your eyes
sum - mer nights

and

ev - 'ry - thing___ is gon - na turn out right.___

72